Answers: Pages P.5 – P.7

2) a) Qualitative
   b) Quantitative
   c) Quantitative
   d) Qualitative
3) a) Discrete
   b) Any discrete data set, e.g. number of pupils in a class.
   c) Continuous data is data that can take any value in an interval.
   d) Any continuous data set, e.g. times, heights, weights, etc.
4) a) Any item of data that cannot be measured numerically, e.g. music types, types of format sold, names of customers, etc.
   b) Any item of data that can be measured numerically, e.g. takings for each day, prices of CDs, amounts spent by customers, etc.
5) a) Discrete
   b) Continuous
   c) Discrete
   d) Continuous
6) a) Data that's made up from two variables.
   b) Discrete bivariate data
   c) Continuous bivariate data

Classifying Data P.5
1) a) 0, 6, 11 and 16
   b) 0-5, 6-10, 11-15 and 16-30
2) a)

Length of time (mins)	1-10	11-20	21-30	31-40	41-50	51-60
Number of people	5	10	5	5	3	2

   b) You lose some of the accuracy in the data.
3) a) A categorical scale of measurement is a scale of measurement using numbers or names which have no meaning other than as class labels.
   b) i) A categorical scale of measurement.
      ii) No — the numbers only represent the type of burger.
4) a) E.g. they are not well defined — they depend on the taste of the person putting the clothes into the classes.
   b) The 5 classes should be well-defined and cover all possibilities, e.g. Tops, Trousers, Jackets, Shoes and Other.

Census Data and Sampling P.6-7
1) A population is a group of things under consideration in any statistical investigation.
2) A sample frame is a list or map of every single member of the population you are sampling from.
3) a) All 20- to 30-year-old women
   b) All the public parks in London
   c) All the squirrels in Britain
   d) All football players in the Premier League
4) a) A census is when you collect data about every member of a population.
   b) A sample is some members of a population.
   c) A sample frame is a list of all the members in a population.
5) E.g. it's often more practical to collect than census data. / It's cheaper to collect. / It's quicker to collect.
6) a) All the lakes and council-owned ponds in Nottingham.
   b) Either a list or a map showing all the lakes and council-owned ponds in Nottingham.
7) a) All the residents of Lancashire
   b) It would be very time-consuming and expensive to question every resident in Lancashire.
8) a) Census data gives information about every single member of a population — it is possible that a sample will not be representative of the population it is drawn from.
   b) The phone book might not cover the whole population. Only choosing names from the phone book excludes people who are ex-directory or who don't own a telephone. This makes the sample biased.
9) a) All the moorland dung beetles in the UK
   b) Because it would be extremely difficult and impractical for him to be sure that he had investigated every single moorland dung beetle in the UK.
10) E.g. Reason 1 — The average wage of three people who are the same age might not be representative of the whole population — e.g. a 13-year-old will probably earn less than a 19-year-old.
    Reason 2 — the sample is very small, so it is extremely unlikely to be representative of the of the population.
11) a) All the supporters of Whitby F.C.
    b) All people on the electoral register of Whitby
    c) E.g. not everyone on the electoral register will support Whitby F.C. / Some supporters may not be on Whitby's electoral register (e.g. because they're too young or live elsewhere).
12) Their samples were chosen at random from the sample frame, so some random variation is likely to occur. This is called variability between samples.

ANSWERS

4

Answers: P.8 — P.10

Simple Random Sampling P.8

1) Choosing something at random means every item in the population has an equal chance of being chosen.

2) A computer and calculator.

3) Number the names in the list from 1 to 4000. Use a computer or calculator or random number tables to generate 500 different random numbers between 1 and 4000. The sample will be the 500 names with those numbers.

4) The places have already been numbered. Use the number list to choose the sample but ignore any numbers that are too large or repeated. The sample is: Cardiff, Truro, Canterbury, Lancaster, Leeds.

5) a) The sample is not random and so might not be representative of all the cakes.

b) E.g. Number all the cakes from 1 to 50 reading across each row. Choose the first 5 numbers reading across the random number table, and take the last two digits from each number. Ignore any numbers that are outside the range 1-50 or repeated. The random numbers are 09, 16, 37, 32, 15. Match the random numbers to the cake weights. The cake weights are 203 g, 198 g, 201 g, 195 g, 189 g.

Stratified and Systematic Sampling P9

1) Number all the phone numbers 1 to 20,000. Divide 20,000 by 500 to get 40. Select a number at random between 1 and 40 — it could be 32. The sample would be the 32nd person on the list, then every 40th person until you have 500 people.

2) Number all the products 1 to 5000. Divide 5000 by 100 to get 50. Select a number at random between 1 and 50 — it could be 12. The sample would be the 12th spring in the batch, then every 50th spring in the batch.

3) a) Total number of staff = 1000. So, rounding to the nearest person, the sample would include:
$(99/1000) \times 100 = 9.9$ — 10 receptionists,
$(53/1000) \times 100 = 5.3$ — 5 salon managers,
$(251/1000) \times 100 = 25.1$ — 25 colour technicians
$(597/1000) \times 100 = 59.7$ — 60 stylists.

b) Because a stratified sample is likely to be more representative of the company's staff.

4) a) So that each year group's representation in the sample is proportional to the size of the year.

b) Total number of students = 1600. $(398 \div 1600) \times 40 = 9.95$ Rounded to the nearest person there would be 10 Year 7 students in the sample.

c) Total number of students = 1600. $199/1600 \times$ size of sample = 10 So, $10 \div (199/1600) = 80.4$ So there are 80 people in the sample.

5) a) i) Number of males in the sample = $(943/2000) \times 50$ = 23.58
Number of male waiting staff in the sample = $(297/943) \times 23.58$ = 7.42 — 7 male waiting staff.
ii) Number of females in the sample = $(1057/2000) \times 50$ = 26.43.
Number of female bar staff in the sample = $(202/1057) \times$ 26.43 (from number of females) = 5.05 — 5 female bar staff.

b) Total number of staff = 2000. $398/2000 \times$ size of sample = 20 So, $20 \div (398/2000) = 100.5$ So there are 101 people in the sample.

Cluster, Quota and Convenience Sampling P.10

1) a) Quota sampling.
b) Convenience sampling.

2) Each town in the county could be a cluster. So use the map to randomly select a sample of towns. Then sample all the houses in those towns.

3) a) They could place an interviewer in the park and ask them to interview the first 500 people that they come across.
b) The sample is biased – wherever the interviewer stands will be closer to some rides than others, so it is more likely that the people selected will prefer those rides.

4) Cluster sampling and quota sampling.

5) 0.7% of 1000 is 7

Answers: P.11 — P.14

Strengths and Weaknesses of Sampling P.11

1) A systematic sample could miss out the faulty tubs.

2) a) Simple random sampling.
   b) Advantage – It will produce an unbiased sample.
   Disadvantage – The households in the sample could be very spread out geographically, so the survey might take a long time and cost a lot.

3) a) Cluster sampling.
   b) The type of accommodation available in just one district might not be representative of all the accommodation in Cumbria.

4) a) Convenience sampling.
   b) The sample could be biased towards people who eat a lot of fast food.

5) a) method 1
   b) The sample is only taken from those parents who drop their children off at school. Other parents are excluded.
   c) Stratified random sampling.

6) E.g. subgroups can be hard to define / it can be expensive because of the extra detail involved.

7) a) When no sample frame is available.
   b) Quota sampling can be easily biased — the sample chosen depends on the interviewer.

Biased Samples P.12

1) a) Reason 1 – They have only included students from one sixth-form college, and excluded all the other sixth-forms in the UK.

Reason 2 – Not all students at the college will be doing chemistry, so the results won't fairly represent the population of chemistry students.
   b) They should have sampled from all sixth-form chemistry students in the UK.

2) a) This is a convenience sample and is not random — it excludes any residents who don't shop in Cheapeez or who weren't in the 200 people who went to the shops on that Saturday.
   b) They should have sampled from all the residents of Devon.

3) a) The sample is biased because it excludes people not shopping on the high street. The proportions of the different age groups in the sample are different to the proportions in the whole of Yeovil, so it doesn't fairly represent the population of Yeovil.
   b) The council should have sampled from all the residents of Yeovil.

4) a) Simple random sampling.
   b) All the people in the sample have an equal chance of being chosen — it's random.

5) a) Fred's sample is non-random – the people in it are likely to be commuters and are also people that already use public transport. So, it doesn't fairly represent the whole population.
   b) Fred should use a simple random sample – e.g. a random sample chosen from the whole population of his town.

Surveys — Questionnaires One P.13

1) E.g. People might forget or be late sending the questionnaires back.

2) E.g. it's likely that the response rate will be very low and only people who have a very strong opinion will respond.

3) a) E.g. they are very cheap to produce.
   b) E.g. they might not sample the correct population because not everyone has access to the internet, which will produce a biased sample.

4) a) Advantage: It's easy to reach a large area (the students could come from anywhere in the country).
   Disadvantage: The students may have moved so the addresses might be out of date.
   b) E.g. they could offer an incentive to respond to the questionnaire. They could follow up people that haven't responded to the questionnaire.

5) a) E.g. People might leave before they have received a questionnaire.
   b) E.g. some people might forget to fill them in / not want to travel back to the sports centre to hand them in.

6) a) The data could be biased because of the low response to the questionnaire, e.g. only people who really like music might be bothered to respond.
   b) He could follow up the people who have not responded.

Surveys — Questionnaires Two P.14

1) a) The question is subjective – "very often" can mean different things to different people.
   b) Any sensible answer, e.g. "How many times a week do you visit the school canteen?"
   0☐ 1☐ 2☐ 3☐ 4☐ 5☐

Answers: P.15 — P.17

2) **a)** How do you travel to school?

b) How do you travel to school? Tick one of the boxes.

Bus ☐ Car ☐ Bicycle ☐ Walk ☐ Other ☐

3) This question is not relevant to what the council wants to find out.

4) **a)** The question is ambiguous — people might answer it in different ways e.g. someone who's 30 could answer in either the 18-30 or 30-40 group. The question doesn't allow for all possible answers e.g. there is no over 60 group.

b) E.g. change the answers to:
   i) Under 18
   ii) 18 to 30
   iii) 31 to 40
   iv) 41 to 60
   v) over 60".

5) **a)** The question is biased towards Milkychoc chocolate.

b) Ask an unbiased question such as, "What is your favourite type of chocolate?"

Surveys — Questionnaires Three P.15

1) **a)** A pilot study is when you test your questionnaire on a small group before sending it out to the sample.

b) It's a good way to spot any problems with the questionnaire before it gets sent out.

2) Opinion scales give more detail than a simple yes/no answer.

3) **a)** E.g. "How satisfied are you with the choice of books in the library? Give an answer between 1 and 5 where 1 means very unsatisfied and 5 means very satisfied."

b) E.g. "Rate the standard of the food in the canteen. Give an answer between 1 and 5 where 1 means very poor and 5 means very good."

4) **a)** Discrete scale.
   b) Continuous linear scale.

5) Questions that people are likely to answer untruthfully.

6) E.g. Toss a coin. If the coin lands on heads tick yes. If the coin lands on tails answer the question. Do you currently smoke cigarettes?
Yes ☐   No ☐

7) You expect about 500 students to have answered yes because their coin showed heads. So 500 of the yes answers can be ignored. This leaves 632 − 500 = 132 out of 500 people who have answered yes to the question of interest.
$(132 \div 500) \times 100 = 26.4\%$
So an estimate of the proportion of students who eat one or more bars of chocolate every day is 26.4%.

Surveys — Interviews P.16

1) **a)** Interview (because it's a complex question).

b) Questionnaire (as it's asking the person to tick a box).

c) Interview (as it's a complex question that could have many answers and the answers can be followed up).

d) Interview (as it's a complex question that might be interpreted differently by different people e.g. some people might think it only means competitive sport).

e) Questionnaire (as it's a simple yes/no question).

2) Because people who have knowingly broken the law are likely to lie about it to an interviewer.

3) ...

4) **a)** Because it is an open complex question, that could have lots of answers.

b) E.g. They can be very expensive. They can take a long time to carry out.

5) **a)** E.g. face-to-face interviews allow you to ask more complex questions / the response rate for interviews tends to be higher.

b) E.g. it's a lot cheaper and easier to sample a large area over the phone than in person. It's easier to survey a larger sample because it's quicker to phone round people than travel to interview them.

Observing and Recording Data P.17

1) **a)** Pupils' favourite drink at lunchtime, number of people living in each pupil's household.

b) E.g.

Number of people living in pupil's house.	Tally	Total (frequency)
2		
3		
4		
5		
6 or more		

c) Pupils' heights — nearest cm. Time taken to travel to school — nearest minute. Weights of pupil's pencil cases — nearest gram.

2)

Sport	Tally	Total (frequency)
Football		
Rugby		
Tennis		
BMX Biking		
Other		

ANSWERS

3) a) Abbie's — her measurements use a more sensible level of precision because most tea towels are less than a metre in length and width.

b) Width — smallest value is 29.5 cm, biggest value is 30.5 cm. Length — smallest value is 39.5 cm, biggest value is 40.5 cm.

4) a) Data logging.

b) It would be too dangerous for a human to measure the temperature.

5) a) Each box could pass over a weighing machine which would be programmed to automatically collect the results.

b) Because it's free from human error.

c) E.g. it's more efficient because someone doesn't need to weigh each box of cereal.

Experiments — Variables P.18

1) Type of hot drink and age.

2) a) The speed at which people drive.

b) E.g. the type of car driven / the age of the driver / the gender of the driver / the weather conditions.

c) So you can be sure that any changes in the response variable are due to changes in the explanatory variable only.

3) E.g. the temperature of the toffee.

4) a) The age of the children.

b) The number of packets of crisps eaten in a month.

c) E.g. the gender of the children / the children's weight / the area that the children live in.

5) a) The weight added to the spring.

b) The extension of the spring.

6) a) air humidity

b) The rate of growth of the plant.

c) E.g. temperature / type of plant investigated / amount of water.

Experiments — Lab, Field and Natural P.19

1) Laboratory, field, natural.

2) a) Natural experiment

b) Laboratory experiment

c) Field experiment

3) The children may behave differently in a laboratory.

4) a) E.g. it would be unethical to force students to do too much or too little exercise.

b) E.g. the students may not complete the exercise diaries honestly.

5) a) Field experiment.

b) The customers may behave differently because the manager is present.

More On Experiments and Design P.20

1) It's when the population is paired up based on certain criteria before being treated.

2) a) There are enough tablets for 52 people (730 ÷ 14). But, since there are a total of 100 people in the test, it would be sensible to give the tablets to half of the group (i.e. 50 people).

b) The remainder should form a control group and so wouldn't receive any treatment.

c) Any sensible answers, including:
i) Number of tablets taken
ii) Time of day that the pills are taken.
iii) Diet of volunteers

3) a) To ensure the experiment is fair.

b) E.g by taking several measurements of her heart rate and working out an average for the results.

4) Patch, week 2, 200.8 — it's not measured to the nearest gram. Patch, week 5, 54 — the value is too small. Felix, week 4, 837 — the value is too big.

5) a) The two coaches could have different ideas about what makes a good serve.

b) The coaches could agree on the things that make a good serve before observing. Then they could compare notes on each serve after observing and agree on a score.

6) a) You could take the mean score from tests before the summer holiday and compare it with the mean score from tests afterwards.

b) The mean score before the summer holiday is 67.7 and after the holiday is 58.6. You could conclude from these results that students do forget subject knowledge over the summer holidays. But, to say this with any confidence you'd need a larger sample size (e.g. 100 students).

Simulation P.21

1) a) The table should be filled in with random 3-digit numbers from your calculator.

b) Any sensible method, e.g. You could call '1' heads and '2' tails. Reading across the table, and ignoring other digits, it would start T,T. / Do the same but only looking at the first digit of each 3-digit random number. / Use all the digits in the table, read from left to right. This time let odd digits be heads, and even digits be tails. This is efficient as it includes all digits available.

Answers: P.22 — P.25

2) a) 0

b)

1st Dice	4	4	3	3	3	3	2	6	5	1
2nd Dice	3	1	2	1	4	4	4	5	4	3
TOTAL	7	5	5	4	7	7	6	11	9	4

c) Her conclusion is incorrect as there are also six 4's. A much more reliable result could be obtained by using a larger sample size, e.g. 100

d) 7 is the most common theoretical total, but there aren't enough 'rolls' to draw a confident conclusion from this test.

Mixed Questions P.22-23

1) a) primary data

b) i) Any two of e.g. the survey is sampling the wrong population — it's excluding people who live in the village but who don't use the library. / It is possible that they will survey the same people twice if people come in to return the books they've borrowed. / It is likely that people who use the library already think that the range of books is OK.

ii) E.g. the librarian could send a questionnaire to all the houses in the village.

c) i) A closed question has a fixed number of possible responses.

ii) E.g. they're easier to process.

d) i) E.g. it doesn't allow for all answers.

ii) qualitative

2) a) E.g. it's often quicker / it's more practical.

b) i) (200/942) × 75 = 15.9
So 16 year 11s should be chosen.

ii) (98/942) × 75 = 7.8
So 8 girls should be chosen.

c) i) random response

ii) 114 of the 200 students answered yes. Around half of the 200 students will have tossed a head and answered yes for that reason. So, it's likely that around 14 of 100 students have cheated in an exam, which means it's likely that about 28 students have cheated.

3) a) i) The employees' performance.

ii) E.g. what the employees had for breakfast.

b) i) E.g. the employees may not be honest about whether they have done the exercise. / It would be difficult for the employees to measure their own performance.

ii) Hayley could conduct an experiment to compare a week with exercise to a week without exercise. For the first week, she could supervise half an hour of exercise before work and then monitor her employees' performance throughout the day. For the second week, she would monitor the performances in the same way.

4) a) All the people who visit the cinema.

b) i) convenience sampling

ii) E.g. it is unlikely to produce a representative sample.

c) E.g. if people filled out the questionnaire at home then it might be inconvenient for them to travel to the cinema to hand it back.

d) E.g. provide an incentive for people to complete the questionnaire, such as entering those people in a raffle.

e) E.g. assign the numbers 1 to 100 to the different films — 1-42 = film 1, 43-56 = film 2, 57-69 = film 3, 70-100 = film 4.

Generate five random numbers from the table — read across the table from left to right, using the last two digits from each number and counting '00' as '100'. The numbers are 86, 78, 07, 99, 37. Match the random numbers to the films. So, 86 = film 4, 78 = film 4, 07 = film 1, 99 = film 4, 37 = film 1.

Section Two — Tabulation and Representation

Frequency Tables P.24

1) a)

Pool Balls	0	1	2	3	4	5	6	7
Tally	JHT I	IIII	III	III	I	I	I	II
Frequency	6	4	3	3	1	1	1	2

b) 21

c) No. The table doesn't tell you how many times she won, because even if none of her balls were left, you can't tell if she potted the black before her opponent.

2) a) 14

b) 8

c)

Number of birds	0	1	2	3	4	5	6	7	8	9
Tally			I	II	IIII	II	II	II	I	
Frequency	0	0	1	2	4	2	2	2	1	0

d) 4

e) 68

Grouped Frequency Tables P.25

1)

Score (s)	Tally	Frequency
3.0<s≤3.5	I	1
3.5<s≤4.0		0
4.0<s≤4.5	I	1
4.5<s≤5.0	I	1
5.0<s≤5.5	II	2
5.5<s≤6.0	III	3
6.0<s≤6.5	II	2
6.5<s≤7.0	III	3
s>7.0	II	2

2) E.g.

Score (s)	Tally	Frequency
Less than 10	IIII	5
10 – 19	IIII IIII IIII	15
20 – 29	IIII	4
30 – 39	II	2
40 and above	IIII I	6

3) The class intervals are not well defined. For example, it is not clear if the year 1995 is included in the first or second class.

Summarising and Interpreting Data P.26

1) **a)** 13
b) 12
c) This data does support the statement because there are more men who are over 1.9 m tall married to women who are over 1.8 m tall, than men who are over 1.9 m tall married to women who are less than 1.8 m tall.

2) E.g.

Width (cm)	Height (cm)		
	$h \le 12$	$12 < h \le 18$	$h > 18$
$w \le 12$	4	0	0
$12 < w \le 18$	4	7	0
$w > 18$	0	1	4

3) **a)** 24%
b) $17 + 16 + 15 + 28 = 76\%$
c) i) The percentage of people eating more than 4 portions of fruit and vegetables after the talk doesn't change.
ii) On days 8 and 9 the percentage of people eating less than two portions of fruit and vegetables decreases. On day 10 it returns to the same level as before the talk.

Simplifying and Analysing Data P.27

1) **a)**

Distance (m)	0 – 10	11 – 20	21 – 30	31 – 40	41 – 50	51 – 60
Frequency	3	12	11	4	1	1

b) Rounding might have resulted in some of the distances being put in the wrong class. For example, a distance of 10.4 m is greater than 10 m, but after rounding it would be put in the 0 – 10 class.

c)

Distance (m)	0 – 20	21 – 40	41 – 60
Frequency	15	15	2

d) The first and second groups now have the same frequencies. This masks the fact that most of the distances were between 11 and 30 metres.

2) **a)**

Year	2006	2007	2008	2009
Total	167	184	203	217

b) The total number of animals sold increased each year.
c) All the detail about the sales of individual animals has been lost. The original table shows that the only animals that have increased their sales each year are rabbits. These large increases have caused the increase in totals. However, the number of stick insects sold has actually fallen each year.

Bar Charts P.28-29

1) **a)** 3
b) 5
c)

Monday	🥐🥐🥐
Tuesday	🥐🥐
Wednesday	🥐🥐🥐🥐🥐
Thursday	🥐🥐🥐
Friday	🥐🥐🥐🥐

2)

3) **a)** Monday, Wednesday and Thursday.
b) Monday
c) Because a composite bar chart would show the total customers for each day as the bars are stacked on top of each other. So, you could easily read the totals from the top of the bar.

4) **a)** 28% (26-30 acceptable)
b) Other answers were given that have not been included in the diagram.
c) The diagram shows a decrease in the % of people feeling that crime increased. This does not mean that fewer people thought this. There may not have been the same number of people in the sample each year.

5) **a)** The number of people smoking is decreasing for both genders.
b) About 10 000 more women smoked.
c) The long term trend shows that the difference in numbers of men and women smoking has decreased.

6) **a)** 60%
b) About 52%
c) Any sensible answer, including:
i) The total number of people in each gender group may be different, yet the numbers of married men and women could be the same.
ii) Jenny might be assuming that men and women marry within the same age range.
d) On average, women live longer than men, and the husbands are usually older. So, women in their 90s are far more likely to have lost their husbands than men in their 90s are to have lost their wives.

Pie Charts P.30

1) Angle per pupil = 360°/45 = 8°

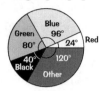

2) Office B, because the area of their pie chart is bigger than the area of the pie chart for office A.

3) a) clothes

b) area of boys' pie chart = πr^2 = $\pi 1.5^2$ = 7.07 cm² (2 d.p.)
7.07/30 = 0.24 cm² (2 d.p.) per person. So, area of girls' pie chart = 50 × 0.24 = 11.78 cm² (2 d.p.)
πr^2 = 11.78, r^2 = 3.75, r = 1.94 cm (2 d.p.)

4) First work out the angle per pupil:

Year Group	Pupils	Angle / pupil
10	30	360°÷ 30 = 12° per pupil
11	20	360°÷ 20 = 18° per pupil

Then work out the angles:

Will watch the match?	Year 10 frequencies	Angle to represent response
Definitely	6	6 × 12° = 72°
Very Likely	4	4 × 12° = 48°
Likely	2	2 × 12° = 24°
Unlikely	8	8 × 12° = 96°
No Way	10	10 × 12° = 120°

Will watch the match?	Year 11 frequencies	Angle to represent response
Definitely	4	4 × 18° = 72°
Very Likely	10	10 × 18° = 180°
Likely	6	6 × 18° = 108°
Unlikely	0	0°
No Way	0	0°

Now draw a pie chart for Year 11 with these angles (and a radius of 3 cm — see next page).
Work out the area:
πr^2 = 3.14 × 3² = 28.26 cm².
So the area per person in this pie chart is 28.26 cm² ÷ 20 people = 1.413 cm² per person.

Use this to work out the area then the radius of the Year 10 pie chart:
Area: 1.413 cm² per person × 30 pupils = 42.39 cm²
πr^2 = 42.39 cm²
So r = √(42.39/3.14) = 3.7 cm.

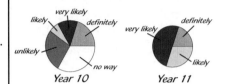

Transforming Data P.31

1) Total sweets = 6 + 18 + 12 = 36
So 1 sweet = 10°
Red = 6 ×10° = 60°
Blue = 18 × 10° = 180°
Green = 12 × 10° = 120°

2) Work out the percentage for each angle:
News = 54°/360° = 15%
Sport = 18°/360° = 5%
Social Networking = 126°/360° = 35%
Blogs = 36°/360° = 10%
Other = 126°/360° = 35%
Change the percentages to numbers:
News = 0.15 × 200 = 30
Sport = 0.05 × 200 = 10
Social Networking = 0.35 × 200 = 70
Blogs = 0.1 × 200 = 20
Other = 0.35 × 200 = 70

Plot the bar chart:

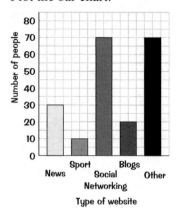

Discrete Data and Frequency Graphs P.32

1) a) 8

b)
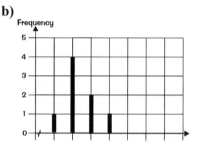

c) 7

2) a)

No. of Words	5	6	7	8	9	10	11
Tally	ll	₩	₩ l	lll	ll	l	l
Frequency	2	5	6	3	2	1	1
Cum Frequency	2	7	13	16	18	19	20

b)
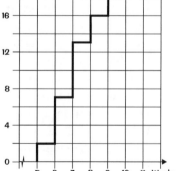

c) 19

ANSWERS

Answers: P.33 — P.37

Continuous Data and Frequency Graphs P.33

1)

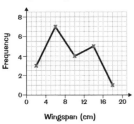

2) a)

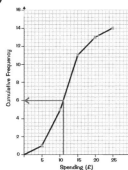

b) Six times. (Draw vertical line at £11 and read value from *y*-axis.)

3) a) 14

b)

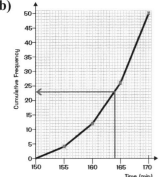

c) 23 people. (Draw vertical line at 164 minutes and read value from *y*-axis.)

Histograms & Frequency Distributions P.34-35

1) a) 08:00 – 09:00: f.d. = 100 cars ÷ 1 hr = 100 cars per hr
09:00 – 12:00: f.d. = 90 cars ÷ 3 hrs = 30 cars per hr
12:00 – 14:00: f.d. = 80 cars ÷ 2 hrs = 40 cars per hr
14:00 – 15:30: f.d. = 75 cars ÷ 1.5 hrs = 50 cars per hr

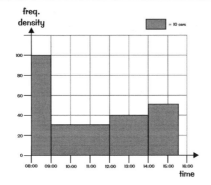

b) The frequency density of 150 represents 75 cars in half an hour. 75/30 = 2.5 cars per minute.

2) a) Frequency density = 1/20 = 0.05 (2 d.p.)

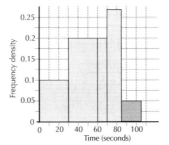

b) (0.2 × 20) + (0.1 × 30) = 4 + 3 = 7, so about 7 goats did it in less than 50 seconds.

3) a) Spinners A&B:
i) Symmetric distribution
ii) Range = 9 – 5 = 4
iii) Mode = 7
iv) Median = 7

b) Spinners C&D:
i) Positive skew
ii) Range = 9 – 5 = 4
iii) Mode = 5
iv) Median = 6

c) Spinners E&F:
i) Negative skew
ii) Range = 8 – 5 = 3
iii) Mode = 7 and 8
iv) Median = 7

4)

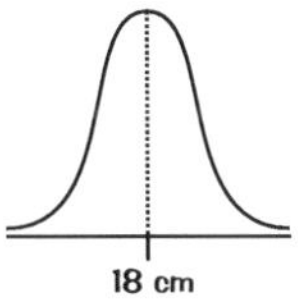

5) a) Totals are:
A: 1000, B: 1950 (allow ±10),
C: 1500 (allow ±10)

b) Proportions are:
A: 600/1000 = 3/5
B: 650/1950 = 1/3
C: 500/1500 = 1/3
So, village A has the highest proportion of people in their 60s. (which is pretty obvious from the diagram.)

c) Village A: Symmetric
Village B: Positive skew
Village C: Negative skew

Stem and Leaf Diagrams P.36

1) a)

7	0
6	1, 6
5	0, 2, 2, 9
4	3, 4, 5, 5, 5, 8
3	1, 2, 7

KEY: 7|0 = 70 seconds

b) Mode = 45 seconds

c) Range = 39 seconds

2) a) 38

b) 4/12 = 1/3

c) 31

d) The girls tend to have less friends on the social networking site than the boys.

3) a)

French		Biology
7	3	1 7
5 4	4	3 3 5 5 5 8
5 2 2 0 0	5	0 0 2 2 2 9
8 7 6 2	6	0 1 6
9 6 1 0	7	0
8 5	8	

Key for French: 7 | 3 = 37
Key for Biology: 3 | 1 = 31

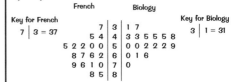

b) 88 – 37 = 51

c) (50 + 50) ÷ 2 = 50

d) The class did better at French because the stem and leaf diagram shows over half the students scored 60 or more in French but only four students did this in Biology.

Population Pyramids and Choropleth Maps P.37

1) a) Ollington

b) 200-299 people/km^2

c) Samley, Robwich

Answers: P.38 — P.41

2) a) Broughtonia:
6.8+6.3+6.0+6.8+6.1+5.9 =
37.9% (±0.5%)
Moorland:
2.4+2.4+2.8+2.2+2.2+2.7 =
14.7% (±0.5%)

b) Broughtonia has a much higher proportion of young. So the birth rate is probably higher, and the death rate is probably higher too.

c) i) male: 2.2+2+1.2+0.5 = 5.9 % (±0.5%)

ii) female: 2.7+2.3+1.5+0.7 = 7.2% (±0.5%)

d) Females tend to live longer in Moorland.

e) The birth rate has fallen over the last 20 years.

Scatter Diagrams P.38

1) parts **a)** and **b)** are shown on the graph.

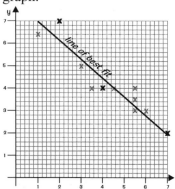

c) As x increases, y decreases. There is a negative correlation between x and y.

2) a)

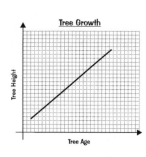

b)

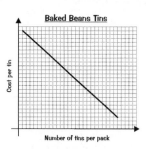

c) no correlation

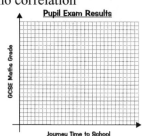

Time Series P.39

1) a) Seasonal fluctuations are regular, repeating patterns in a time series.

b) i) no trend.
ii) upward trend.
iii) downward trend.

2) a)

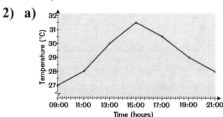

b) The graph shows an upward trend until 15.00 hours and then a downward trend.

3) a)

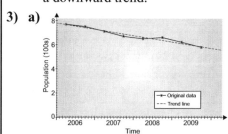

b) The trend line shows a downward trend.

c) 560 (accept answer consistent with graph)

More Diagrams, Problems and Errors P.40-41

1) a) The pictograms are only correct if you round the data to the nearest 50 million BTU/person/year (it looks like the Thereabouts use 7 times as much energy per person as Here-nor-there, but it's actually over 10 times as much).

b) According to the data the Thereabouts pictogram should have two and a half people symbols, and the Here-nor-there pictogram 5½, not 2½

2) a) You can't really agree or disagree unless you look at the original data. An average temperature of 0 °C for April would seem very unlikely, as it would mean that the temperature would be below zero for around half of the time in this month. However, you would need to check the original data before being certain.

b) The uneven scaling makes it look as if the temperature rise from May to June and from June to July is greater than from July to August, when in fact it's the same.

3) a) Correct: Pair 1, Pair 2, Pair 5
Misleading: Pair 3, Pair 4

b) PAIR 3: The 2nd practice diagram has an area four times that of the first. This is not representative of the target being hit twice as often.
PAIR 4: The 2nd diagram has a volume 8 times as large as the 1st. Again this is misleading.

4) Area of Kayleigh's circle:
$\pi \times 3^2 = 9\pi$
So, the area of Amy's circle is:
$9\pi \times 3 = 27\pi$.
Radius (r) of Amy's circle:
$\pi r^2 = 27\pi$
$r = \sqrt{27} = 5.196$ cm
So, the diameter = 10.4 cm

Answers: P.42 — P.45

Mixed Questions P42-43

1) a)

Height, (cm)	$150 \le x < 160$	$160 \le x < 170$	$170 \le x < 180$	$180 \le x < 190$	$190 \le x < 200$
Team A	0	1	2	7	1
Team B	1	4	5	1	0

b) i)

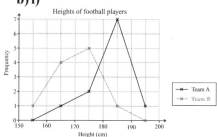

Heights of football players

ii) Most of Team A's polygon lies further to the right than Team B's.

c) i)

Height, x (cm)	$x < 160$	$x < 170$	$x < 180$	$x < 190$	$x < 200$
Cumulative frequency	1	5	10	11	11

ii)

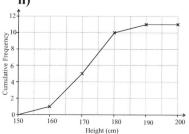

Remember that you plot the cumulative frequency against the upper boundary of each class, not the midpoint of the class.

2) a)

Length (l) cm	Frequency
$6 < l \le 8$	3
$8 < l \le 9$	5
$9 < l \le 10$	5
$10 < l \le 11$	7
$11 < l \le 12$	7
$12 < l \le 15$	6
Total	33

b) Advantage — e.g. it makes the data easier to handle.
Disadvantage — e.g. you lose some of the detail of the data.

c) First work out the frequency densities:

Length (l) cm	Frequency	Frequency density
$6 < l \le 8$	3	1.5
$8 < l \le 9$	5	5
$9 < l \le 10$	5	5
$10 < l \le 11$	7	7
$11 < l \le 12$	7	7
$12 < l \le 15$	6	2
Total	33	

Then draw your histogram:

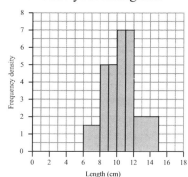

d) The last bar includes the relevant length range. So use, frequency = frequency density × class width = $2 \times 2 = 4$.
This means approximately 4 people guessed 13 cm or higher.

3) a) i) Area of South West pie chart
$= \pi r^2 = \pi \times 3^2 = 28.27$ cm^2
(2 d.p.) So, area per unit $= 28.27 \div 2880 = 0.00982$ cm^2
So, area of North East pie chart
$= 0.00982 \times 3420$
$= 33.58$ (2 d.p) $= \pi r^2$
So, $r = \sqrt{(33.58 \div \pi)}$
$= 3.27 = 3.3$ cm

ii)

Distance (d) travelled, km	North East	
	Number of people (in thousands)	Angle °
$0 \le d < 2$	1273	**134**
$2 \le d < 5$	608	**64**
$5 \le d < 10$	532	**56**
$10 \le d < 20$	475	**50**
$20 \le d < 30$	247	**26**
$d \ge 30$	285	**30**
Totals	3420	360

iii) not to scale

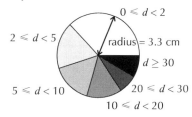

b) Similarity — e.g. the most common distance travelled to work by both the South West and North East commuters is $0 \le d < 2$.
Difference — e.g. a greater proportion of commuters in the North East travel over 30 km to work.

Section Three — Data Analysis

Mean, Median and Mode P.44

1) a) $32.82/20 = 1.64$ m (2 d.p.)
b) 1.65 m
c) 1.65 m

2) $108 - 75 = 33$ years old

3) a) 2 hrs 40 mins.
b) The mean will increase because the value added is greater than the original mean.

4) 5 and 6. As the mean of all the numbers is 6, the total of the 6 numbers must be $6 \times 6 = 36$. So the two missing numbers must add up to 11. The missing numbers must be 5 and 6 so that the middle number is 6.

5) $(0.4 \times 50) + (0.4 \times 65) + (0.2 \times 45) = 55\%$

6) a) Use linear transformations, e.g. multiply by 10 000 then subtract 300. Mean $= 405/10 = 40.5$. Then reverse the transformations so mean $= 0.03405$
b) 0.0343
c) 0.0365

Mean, Median and Mode — Discrete Data P.45

1) $396/12 = 33$
2) a) $122/30 = 4.07$ (2.d.p.)
b) 4.5
c) 5

3) **a)** 685/120 = 5.71 (2 d.p.)

   b) 6

   c) 5

4) **a)** Mean = 1128/120 = 9.4, median = 9, mode = 8.

   b) Mean = 1158/121 = 9.57 (2.d.p.), median = 9, mode = 8.

Mean, Median and Mode — Grouped Data P.46

1) **a)** 10847.5/95 = 114.2 (1 d.p.)

   b) You don't know the original data values any more, so you just have to use the midpoint value of each group.

   c) 111-130

   d) 91-110

2) **a)** Mean. The winner is probably the one who scored more points overall.

   b) Eric. His estimated mean score of 66.15 is bigger than Bill's, which was only 60.5.

3) **a)** 4150/40 = 103.75 kg

   b) $90 < x \leq 110$ kg

   c) $90 < x \leq 110$ kg

4) **a)** 16710/50 = 334.2 cm

   b) $300 < x \leq 330$ cm

   c) E.g. overall position number of median is 25.5 in group $300 < x \leq 330$ cm. Position in group is 25.5 − 5 = 20.5. Proportion of way through group = 20.5/22 = 0.932. 0.932 × 30 = 27.96. So median estimate is 300 + 27.96 = 327.96 = 328 cm (to nearest whole number).

Choosing the Best Average P.47

1) **a)** The median. With such a small sample and a rogue value (90), the mean would be distorted.

   b) The mode. There are no two values the same – and even if there had been it could just be a lucky coincidence.

   c) He should use a much larger sample.

2) It can be used with qualitative data.

3) The median is not distorted by outliers and is easier to find in ordered data.

4) **a)** Mean.

   b) Mode. The mode is the only average that can be found for qualitative data.

   c) Median. More people are likely to visit the theme park on the Bank holiday in August, so there's likely to be an outlier in the data due to that.

5) $\sqrt[4]{1.04 \times 1.08 \times 1.07 \times 1.08} =$ 1.067 = 6.7%

6) Fixed rate of 7.5%. The other rates combine to give 7.49%.

Range, Quartiles, Deciles and Percentiles P.48

1) **a)** 1020 − 80 = 940

   b) 510

   c) 700

   d) 840

2) **a)** 65 g

   b) The 5th decile (or D_5)

   c) 72 g

3) **a)** UQ = 9th number = 38.

   b) The 5th decile is the same as the median = 29.

   c) The 50th percentile is also the median = 29.

4) As the range is 98 and the integers are different, they must be consecutive. The median is 350 so the integers must be 301, 302, ..., 399.

a) LQ = 25th number = 325.

b) D_4 = 40th number = 340.

c) P_3 = 3rd number = 303.

d) The 99th percentile

Interquartile and Interpercentile Range P.49

1) **a)** 300 − 100 = 200

   b) 240 − 160 = 80

2) **a)** 21 cm

   b) Q_3 = 25.5-26 cm
   Q_1 = 16-16.5 cm
   IQR = $Q_3 − Q_1$
   allow answer between 9 and 10 cm.

   c) 14.5 (allow 14.5-15 cm)

   d) D_9 = 31-31.5 cm
   D_1 = 11 cm
   Interdecile range = $D_9 − D_1$
   allow answer between 20 and 20.5 cm

   e) It gives the range of the middle 80% of the data, instead of only the middle 50%, which means that only the most extreme values are excluded.

3) **a)**

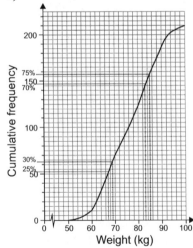

For the following answers accept any answer in line with your graph.

b) i) IQR = 85 – 67 = 18 kg
ii) 68 kg
iii) P_{70} – P_{30} range =
83 – 69 =16 kg

Variance and Standard Deviation P.50-51

1) 1.02
2) **a)** Mean = 68.5
b)

x	x-x̄	(x-x̄)²
64	–4.5	20.25
71	2.5	6.25
68	–0.5	0.25
79	10.5	110.25
62	–6.5	42.25
73	4.5	20.25
67	–1.5	2.25
64	–4.5	20.25

c) Standard Deviation =
$\sqrt{\Sigma(x - \bar{x})^2/n}$ = $\sqrt{222/8}$ = 5.27
3) The spread does not change by adding 10 to all the numbers, so the standard deviation = 2.87.
4) Standard Deviation =
$\sqrt{\Sigma x^2/n - \bar{x}^2}$
= $\sqrt{3840/12 - 17.4^2}$
= 4.15 (2.d.p.)
5) **a)** 85.89 kg
b) Variance = 0.0129 kg
Standard deviation = 0.114 (3.s.f.)
6) **a)** Variance = $[(67/12) - 2.3^2)]$ = 0.293 (3.s.f.)
b) Standard Deviation = 0.54 (2.d.p.)
7) E.g.

x	f	fx	x²	fx²
1	3	3	1	3
2	5	10	4	20
3	4	12	9	36
4	2	8	16	32
5	1	5	25	25
Total	15	38	-	116

a) Mean = 38/15 = 2.533 (3.d.p)
b) Variance = $[(116/15) - 2.533^2)]$ = 1.32 (2.d.p.)
c) Standard Deviation = 1.15 (2.d.p.)
8) **a)** Mean = 1223/40 = 30.575
Variance = $[(37581/40) - 30.575^2)]$ = 4.69 (2.d.p.)
Standard Deviation = 2.17 (2.d.p.)
b) New mean = 1313/43 = 30.535
Variance = $[(40281/43) - 30.535^2)]$ = 4.38 (2.d.p.)
Standard Deviation = 2.09 (2.d.p.)
9) **a)** Mean = 2680/50 = 53.6 cm
Variance = $[(150850/50) - 53.6^2)]$ = 144.04 cm
b) Standard Deviation = 12.00 cm

Box and Whisker Plots P.52

1) **a)** positive skew
b) negative skew
c) symmetrical
2)
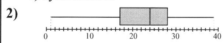
3) **a)** 60 years
b) 65 – 45 = 20 years
c) negative
4) **a)** 25
b) 57 – 7 = 50
c)
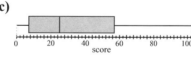
d) positive

More On Box and Whisker Plots P.53

1) **a)** $[21+11 - (2 \times 15)]/(21–11)$ = 0.2, slight positive skew.
b) $[51+11 - (2 \times 16)]/(51–11)$ = 0.75, positive skew.
c) $[59 +19 - (2 \times 49)]/(59–19)$ = –0.5, negative skew.

2) **a)** $3 \times (8 – 9)/1.2 = –2.5$
b) The scores are negatively skewed — the lower half of the scores are more spread out than the upper half of the scores.
3) Outliers are values greater than $39 + 1.5 \times (39 – 27) = 57$ or values less than $27 – 1.5 \times (39 – 27) = 9$. So the value 58 is an outlier.
4) **a)**
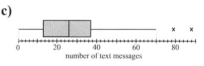
b) 79 and 88.
c)
number of text messages

The Normal Distribution and Standardised Scores P.54

1) **a)** $(61 – 47)/8 = 1.75$
b) $(52 – 58)/6.1 = –0.98$ (2 d.p.)
c) Geography, in which her standardised score is 3.27 (2 d.p.)
d) –0.08 (2 d.p.)
e) Music, in which his standardised score is –2.95 (2 d.p.)
2) 1300 kg (almost all values are within ± 3 standard deviations of the mean).
3) **a)** 47. Her standardised score was 1/6.
b) Laura. The total of her standardised scores was 4/9, whereas Jane's total was 5/18.
4) If 2.5% of the packets weigh less than 485g, this means that 485 must be equal to the mean minus 2 standard deviations. So the standard deviation is approximately $[(500 – 485)/2]$ = 7.5 g

Answers: P.55 — P.59

Comparing Data Sets P.55

1) **a)** C. 50% of the marks were not more than one out and he or she was never more than two out on any one script.

   b) A. More than a quarter of the marks were at least two out and the marks were four out on at least two occasions.

   c) He or she is on average giving the script one less mark than specified so, at the end of the paper if there is a mark in doubt, he or she should award it.

2) **a)** B. The standard deviation was less than A's.

   b) A. The range is greater than B's.

   c) B. The mean is greater than A's.

3) **a)**

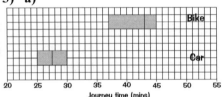

   b) E.g. the median time for people travelling by bike to work is higher than for those travelling by car. So on average it takes people longer to get to work by bike than by car.
   The interquartile range for journey times by car is smaller than the interquartile range for journey times by bike — this suggests that the time taken to get to work by people using a car is less varied than for those cycling.

Summary Statistics P.56-57

1) **a)** 2005
   b) $(112/100) \times 26\,000 = £29\,120$.
   c) $(114/112) \times 29\,400 = £29\,925$
2) $(432/28600) \times 1000 = 15.1$ (1 d.p.)

3) $(15000/1000) \times 21.4 = 321$

4) **a)** The missing price is £815.10. The missing index numbers are 110 and 104 (from left to right).
   b) It shows that the price of the product has increased by 10% from the previous year.
   c) 108.68

5) **a) i)** $(9.90/8.70) \times 100 = 113.8$ (1 d.p.)
   ii) $(15.60/14.40) \times 100 = 108.3$ (1 d.p.)
   iii) $(8.70/7.80) \times 100 = 111.5$ (1 d.p.)
   b) $(113.8 \times 28) + (108.3 \times 47) + (111.5 \times 25) / 100 = 110.6$ (1 d.p.)
   c) It went up by about 10.6%.

6) **a)** 120, 128.
   b) 28%

7) **a)** Hadham is more likely to have a higher crude birth rate as more people are of child-bearing age (16-30 and 31-45).
   b) The standardised birth rate for Hadham is likely to be lower as it takes into account the amount of people in each age group.
   c) Because standardised birth rates take into account the large differences in age distributions.

Time Series P.58-59

1) **a)** 60, 59, 58.33, 58.33, 60, 59, 60
   b) 9.57, 9.57, 9.43, 9.43, 9.57, 10.14, 9.29, 8.14

2) **a)** 108, 109, 110, 112, 114, 114, 115, 116, 118, 120, 121
   b)

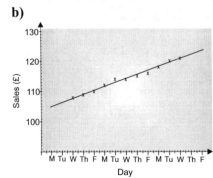

3) **a)**

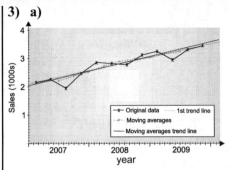

   3560 pairs of shoes
   b) Moving averages are 2212.5, 2387.5, 2525, 2732.5, 2890, 2990, 3022.5, 3152.5 and 3235.
   c) 3620
   d) The line drawn from the moving averages is the most accurate so c) is the most reliable result.

4) **a)**

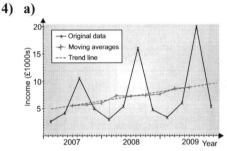

   b) Should be a 4-point moving average. Moving averages are 5575, 5675, 6000, 7375, 7325, 7425, 7575, 8575 and 8725.
   c) See graph
   For the following answers accept any answer in line with your graph.
   d) $3000 - 6400 = -£3400$
   e) $[(2600 - 5000) + (-3400) + (3400-8250)]/3 = -£3550$

5) **a)**

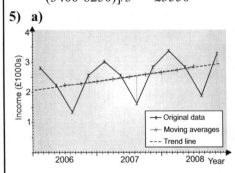

Answers: P.60 — P.63

b) Moving averages are 2235, 2287.5, 2367.5, 2435, 2500, 2592.5, 2660, 2730, 2845.

c) See graph

For the following answers accept any answer in line with your graph.

d) Using trend line shown, seasonal effect = 1620 – 2550 = –£930 (accept answer consistent with graph and between –£950 and –£900)

e) [(2560 – 2330) + (2820 – 2630) + (3280 – 2930)]/3 = £257 (accept answer consistent with graph)

f) 3230 + 257 = £3487 (accept answer consistent with graph)

More Types of Time Series P.60

1) **a)** The output gap was positive between 2004 and 2008. This suggests that the Richenstein economy was in a boom.

b) Prices of goods increase in a boom.

c) Because the output gap became negative in 1997, suggesting that Richenstein was in a recession.

2) **a)** 70

b) 260

c) 880

d) The top line of the Z shows that the popularity of mangos decreased in 2009 compared to the year before.

3) **a)**

	2009					
	Autumn		Spring		Summer	
	1	2	1	2	1	2
	96	92	88	88	94	93
Total since Autumn 2009 half term 1	96	188	276	364	458	551
Total for the past year	526	531	538	545	549	551

b)

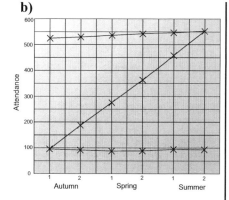

c) The strategy has been successful because the moving total line (the top line of the Z) shows an increase in attendance from the previous year.

Quality Assurance P.61

1) **a)**

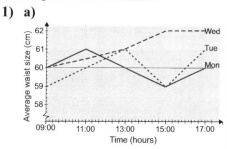

b) Yes. On Wednesday, when the samples taken were always on or above the target level. (Any reasonable answer with explanation is OK.)

2) **a)**

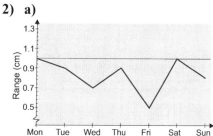

b) No, because all the values are below the acceptable range.

3) Samples 1, 4 and 5 lie between the higher and lower warning limits so the quality of the product is acceptable and no action should have been taken. Samples 2, 3, 6 and 7 lie between the warning and action limits so another sample should have been taken straight away.

Sample 8 lies outside the action limits which means at this point the production should have been stopped and the machine reset.

4) **a)**

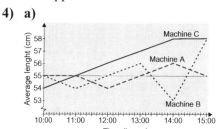

b) Yes.

c) Yes. The machine is becoming very inconsistent — the lengths of the laces are becoming more variable with time. (Any reasonable answer with explanation is OK.)

d) No. The lengths of the laces are increasing. (Any reasonable answer with explanation is OK.)

Correlation P.62-63

1) Correlation is how closely related two things are.

2) **a)** positive correlation

b) no correlation

c) negative correlation

d) no correlation

e) positive correlation

3) A — negative correlation. As temperature increases, sales of thermal underwear decrease.

B — there is no correlation between height and the number of siblings a person has.

C — positive correlation. As the temperature increases, sales of ice cream also increase.

4) The value of 0.75 for the product moment correlation coefficient shows a fairly strong positive correlation, which means that the more friends a person has on a social networking site, the more event invitations they will receive.

5) b) and c)

6) a) C

b) F

c) B

d) G

e) A

f) D

g) E

7) a) C

b) B

c) F

d) D

8)

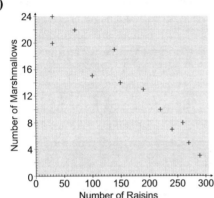

The graph shows negative correlation.

Spearman's Rank Correlation Coefficient P.64

1) −1 to 1

2) −0.1 (it is the closest to zero)

3) a) $1 - (6 \times 40)/(10 \times 99) = 0.76$ (to 2 d.p.)

b) Yes. Not unusually similar though (though this does depend how much the women differ).

4) a) $1 - (6 \times 4)/(7 \times 48)$ $= 0.93$ (2 d.p.)

b) There is a strong positive correlation which means the judges' rankings are in very close agreement.

5) a)

	A	B	C	D	E	F	G	H
Thelma	4.5	6	8	4.5	2.5	1	7	2.5
Louise	3	4	1	5	6	8	2	7

b) $1 - (6 \times 162)/(8 \times 63) = -0.93$ (2 d.p.)

c) They have very different tastes in wine (e.g. preferring red or white wine).

Working with Scatter Diagrams P.65

1) a)

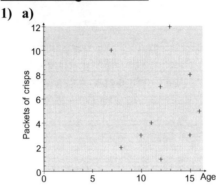

b) No.

2) a) $y = x + 8$

b) The students scored, on average, 8 marks more for paper 2 than paper 1.

3) a)

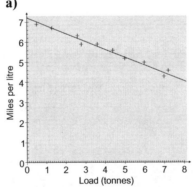

b) Negative correlation. The heavier his load, the more diesel he uses.

c) $m = -2.8/7.2 = -0.39$ (allow $-0.38 - -0.40$), $c = 7.2$ (allow $7.1 - 7.3$) $y = -0.39x + 7.2$

d) The van does about 7.2 miles per litre of diesel unloaded.

Interpolation and Extrapolation P.66

1) a) Interpolation is estimating a value that lies between two known values.

b) Interpolation usually gives a more reliable estimate than extrapolation, since extrapolation involves estimating a value outside the range of the data set it is based on.

2) a)

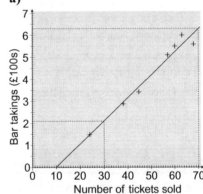

b) £210 (allow between £200 and £220)

c) £630 (allow between £620 and £640)

3) a)

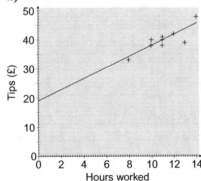

b) $y = 1.9x + 19$. (accept answer consistent with graph)

c) £91 (accept answer consistent with equation above)

d) Her estimate is unlikely to be very accurate, since she is extrapolating a long way outside her data set.

19

Answers: P.67 — P.70

Estimation of Population P.67

1) **a)** 12.25 cm

   b) Any sensible answer, e.g.,
   If the slug population in Hazel's garden is more than a couple of hundred, 10 slugs isn't a reasonable sample and the answer could be way out.
   It's fairly difficult to get an accurate measurement of the length of a slug.
   Hazel may have made a mistake in her measurements.

2) **a)** 40
   b) 1200

3) Capture/recapture (or Petersen's Method).
   Also accept any other reasonable answer.

4) **a)** 20%
   b) More people could have been asked from the same university, but better still would have been if another similar opinion poll had been held at a different university (or several universities) and the results combined.
   c) Most of the students are opposed to top-up fees.

5) **a)** iii) 50 (5 would not be a representative sample, 300 is a bigger sample than you need.)
   b) Sarah-Jayne would have to use four times the sample size.

Capture / Recapture Method P.68

1) **a)** You must assume that:
   the samples have been selected randomly, the samples are representative of the whole population, the population size remains constant, the original sample has had a chance to mix back into the whole population.

   b) 12/30 = 112/N
   So N = 280 fish

2) **a)** Rats: 70/N = 2/50
   So, N = 1750
   b) Mice: 30/N = 3/50
   So, N = 500

3) **a)** 120 foxes and 2000 chickens
   b)i) 147 foxes and 750 chickens
   ii) 500

4) **a)** Capture/recapture would only work well for populations (ii) and (iii).
   b) Population (i) is not contained within the field, so it won't be constant.
   Population (iv) can't move, so the tagged sample will never be able to mix back in with the rest of the population.
   Population (v) grows too fast to measure in this way.

Mixed Questions P.69-70

1) **a)** 56 minutes.
   b) $D_8 = 74$ and $D_2 = 38$, D_8 to D_2 range = 74 − 38 = 36 minutes.

2) **a)** Median, because there's an outlier (112) in the data.
   b)i) The range uses all of the pieces of data including the outliers, which can distort it.
   ii) E.g. the interquartile range because it excludes outliers.
   c) + d)

	Week 1 t (sec)	Week 2 t (sec)	Week 1 rank	Week 2 rank	d	d²
Anna	56	65	3	5	2	4
Becca	62	62	4	4	0	0
Chaz	51	60	1	3	2	4
Dave	64	58	5	1	4	16
Eric	53	59	2	2	0	0

   $r_s = 1 - [(6\sum d^2) \div n(n^2 - 1)]$, and $\sum d^2 = 24$
   So, $r_s = 1 - [(6 \times 24) \div 5(25 - 1)] = -0.2$

   e) Weak negative correlation — i.e. close to no link between the karting and skiing times.

3) **a)** $(6.2 + 4.0 + 4.8) \div 3 = 15 \div 3 = 5.0\ ^\circ C$
   b) $(4.0 + 4.8 + x) \div 3 = 4.8$, so $8.8 + x = 4.8 \times 3$. $x = 5.6\ ^\circ C$
   c) i) & ii)

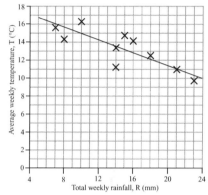

   Weak, negative correlation — meteorology stations having higher rainfall tend to have a lower average weekly temperature.

4) **a)** E.g. for quality control/ assurance.
   b) Yes, the machines should have been reset as almost all of the ranges were outside the target range.
   c) $418 \pm (2 \times 0.7) = 416.6$g to 419.4g
   d) 820 is 2 standard deviations below the mean. 2.5% of values will lie below 820 kg. So 2.5% of 300 = 7.5. So on about 7 or 8 days.

Answers: P.71 — P.74

Section Four — Probability

Probability One P.71

1) A specific thing that has a probability of happening.

2)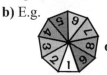

The positions of a, b and c can vary along the scale but should be in the same order.

3) All probabilities lie between 0 and 1, so the probability of Christina passing her exam could at most be 1. A probability of 1.4 is impossible.

4) The three outcomes are: Glenda wins, Gertrude wins, the race is a draw.

5) a) Spinner 1: **i)** 1   **ii)** 2
   Spinner 2: **i)** 2   **ii)** 1
   Spinner 3: **i)** 2   **ii)** 1
   Spinner 4: **i)** 3   **ii)** 4

   b) E.g.

6) a) 1, 2, 3, 4, 5, 6

   b) No. For the method to be fair, both must have an equal probability of winning the ticket. Here 4 out of the 6 possible outcomes would result in Gordon winning, so the probability of him winning is: 4/6 = 2/3 or 0.67 (2 d.p.)

   c) They should have 3 numbers each, e.g. Gordon wins if a 1, 2 or 3 is thrown and Louise wins for a 4, 5 or 6 (any combination will do). They then each have probability 3/6 = 1/2 of winning the ticket.

Probability Two P.72

1) 1/10 or 0.1

2) P(Picks mint sweet) = 1/4 or 0.25
   1/4 = no. of mint sweets ÷ total sweets. 1/4 = 7/total. So, total = 7 × 4 = 28 sweets in the packet.

3) a) 1, 3 and 5 are odd numbers, so probability is 3/6 = 1/2 or 0.5
   b) 1/6 or 0.167 (3 d.p.)
   c) 2, 4 and 6 are even numbers, so probability is 3/6 = 1/2 or 0.5
   d) 2, 3, 5 are prime numbers, so probability is 3/6 = 1/2 or 0.5

4) a) 8 runners are women so probability is 8/24 = 1/3 or 0.33 (2 d.p.)
   b) 16 runners have tracksuits so probability is 16/24 = 2/3 or 0.67 (2 d.p.)
   c) 16 runners are male so probability is 16/24 = 2/3 or 0.67 (2 d.p.)

5) 36% of people are in the age range 25-40 so the probability is 0.36 or 36% or 36/100

6) a) There are 25 odd numbers so probability is 25/50 = 0.5
   b) There are 20 numbers above 30 so the probability = 20/50 = 2/5 or 0.4
   c) She has 5 chances to win so the probability is 5/50 = 1/10 or 0.1

Sample Space Diagrams P.73–74

1)

	Spinner				
Dice	1	2	3	4	5
1	1,1	1,2	1,3	1,4	1,5
2	2,1	2,2	2,3	2,4	2,5
3	3,1	3,2	3,3	3,4	3,5
4	4,1	4,2	4,3	4,4	4,5
5	5,1	5,2	5,3	5,4	5,5
6	6,1	6,2	6,3	6,4	6,5

2)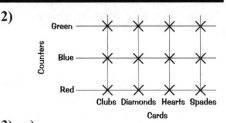

3) a)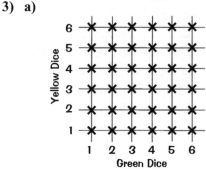

   b) i) 9 pairs of odd numbers out of 36 pairs — 9/36 = 1/4 or 0.25
   ii) 21 pairs add up to less than 8 — 21/36 = 7/12 or 0.583 (3 d.p.)
   iii) 6 pairs have a difference of 3 — 6/36 = 1/6 or 0.167 (3 d.p.)

4) a) 60
   b) 15 + 2 + 3 + 4 = 24
   c) i) 3 want to do all three activities — 3/60 = 1/20 or 0.05
   ii) 14 only want to do orienteering — 14/60 = 7/30 or 0.233 (3 d.p.)

5) a) 21
   b) i) 4/21 or 0.190 (3 d.p.)
   ii) 12/21 = 4/7 or 0.571 (3 d.p.)

6) a) y = 1, x = 2
   b) 2 + 3 + 2 + 1 = 8 people like ginger biscuits so the probability is 8/27 or 0.296 (3 d.p.)
   c) 9/27 = 1/3 or 0.333 (3 d.p.)

7) a)

Type of vehicle	Red	Blue	Green	White	Total
Car	12	12	5	3	32
Lorry	2	1	0	11	14
Motorbike	1	2	0	1	4
Total	15	15	5	15	50

   b) 50

c) i) 2 red lorries so probability is 2/50 = 1/25 or 0.04

ii) 32 cars so probability is 32/50 = 16/25 or 0.64

iii) 0 green motorbikes so probability is 0/50 = 0

iv) 15 blue vehicles so probability is 15/50 = 3/10 or 0.3

Relative Frequency P.75

1) 71/308 or 0.231 (3 d.p.)

2) Green brolly — 9/18 = 1/2 or 0.5

3) **a)**

Number of spins	10	20	50
Number of 1s spun	3	6	13
Relative frequency	0.3	0.3	0.26

b) The one with 50 spins, i.e. 0.26

c) Probably not.

d) For an unbiased spinner, the probability of spinning a one is 1/4 or 0.25. For this spinner the relative frequency is very close to 1/4, so it's unlikely to be biased.

4) **a)** 45/100 = 9/20 or 0.45

b) For an unbiased standard dice, the probability of throwing a 4 is 1/6 = 0.167. But for this dice the estimated probability is 0.45, which is much higher. This suggests that the dice is biased.

5) **a)** estimated probability = relative frequency of wins = 5/20 = 1/4 or 0.25

b) expected frequency of wins is 16 × 1/4 = 4. So Dana is more likely to be right.

Expected and Actual Frequencies P.76

1) **a)** 3/6 × 50 = 150/6 = 25

b) factors of 6 are 1, 2, 3, 6

4/6 × 50 = 200/6 = 100/3 or 33.33 (2 d.p.)

c) 1/6 × 50 = 50/6 = 25/3 or 8.33 (2 d.p.)

2) **a)** 280 × 0.05 = 14

b) 100 × 0.9 = 90

3) **a)**

Outcome	First	Second	Third or worse
Expected Frequency	10 × 0.7 = 7	10 × 0.2 = 2	10 × 0.1 = 1

b)

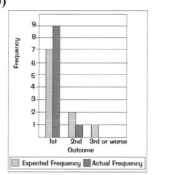

4) **a)** 60 × 0.2 = 12 packets of crisps

b) No, it's not unusual for an expected frequency (0.2 × 5 = 1) to be different from the actual frequency (0) — especially over so few trials.

c) He could buy more packets of crisps.

Probability Laws One P.77

1) **a)** not mutually exclusive

b) mutually exclusive

c) not mutually exclusive

d) mutually exclusive

2) **a)** 3/12 = 1/4 or 0.25

b) 5/12 or 0.417 (3 d.p.)

c) 3/12 + 4/12 = 7/12 or 0.583 (3 d.p.)

3) **a)** 5/14 or 0.357 (3 d.p.)

b) 6/14 + 5/14 = 11/14 or 0.786 (3 d.p.)

c) 1 – P(action or comedy) = 1 – 11/14 = 3/14 or 0.214, since the events 'action or comedy' and 'neither action nor comedy' are exhaustive. Or P(science fiction) = 3/14 or 0.214 (3 d.p.)

4) **a)** 13/52 + 13/52 + 13/52 = 39/52 = 3/4 or 0.75

b) 1 – P(getting a 5) = 1 – 4/52 = 48/52 = 12/13 or 0.923 (3 d.p.)

c) 13/52 + 12/52 – 3/52 = 22/52 = 11/26 or 0.423 (3 d.p.)

d) 4/52 + 13/52 – 1/52 = 16/52 = 4/13 or 0.308 (3 d.p.)

5) probability of Alicia winning = 30/50 = 3/5 or 0.6 probability of Ben winning = 20/50 = 2/5 = 0.4 The events are exhaustive since they are mutually exclusive and their probabilities add up to 1. (Either Alicia wins or Ben wins — there are no other possible outcomes.)

Probability Laws Two P.78

1) 4/52 × 4/52 × 4/52 = 64/140608 or 0.000455 (3 s.f.)

2) 1/6 × 1/6 × 1/6 × 1/6 × 1/6 × 1/6 × 1/6 = 1/279936 or 0.00000357 (3 s.f.)

3) **a)** 1/5 × 1/2 = 1/10 or 0.1

b) 1/5 × 1/2 = 1/10 or 0.1

c) (1/5 × 1/2) + (1/5 × 1/2) = 1/5 or 0.2

4) **a)** 0.4 × 0.7 × 0.9 = 0.252

b) 0.6 × 0.3 × 0.9 = 0.162

5) It's easier to work out the probability of him not burning any cakes and then subtract it from 1. So, 0.85 × 0.85 × 0.85 × 0.85 × 0.85 × 0.85 = 0.377 (3 s.f.). 1 – 0.377 = 0.623

6) **a)** 0.6 × 0.3 = 0.18

b) (0.6 × 0.7) + (0.4 × 0.3) = 0.54

c) 0.4 × 0.7 = 0.28

Answers: P.79 — P.82

Tree Diagrams P.79

1) $0.4 \times 0.7 = 0.28$

2) a)

b) $0.4 \times 0.4 \times 0.4 = 0.064$

c) $0.4 \times 0.4 \times 0.6 = 0.096$

d) Watching any two episodes can happen in three ways:
$0.4 \times 0.4 \times 0.6 = 0.096$
$0.4 \times 0.6 \times 0.4 = 0.096$
$0.6 \times 0.4 \times 0.4 = 0.096$
So, $0.096 + 0.096 + 0.096 = 0.288$

3) a)

b) i) $0.6 \times 0.5 = 0.3$

ii) $0.4 \times 0.5 = 0.2$

4) a) $0.2 \times 0.2 = 0.04$

b) $(0.2 \times 0.2) + (0.3 \times 0.3) = 0.13$

c) $(0.3 \times 0.5) + (0.5 \times 0.3) + (0.5 \times 0.5) + (0.5 \times 0.2) + (0.2 \times 0.5) = 0.75$

Conditional Probability P.80–81

1) a) 30/71 or 0.423 (3 d.p.)

b) 48/120 or 0.4

2) a) 16/56 or 0.286 (3 d.p.)

b) 5/44 or 0.114 (3 d.p.)

3) a) i) $25/60 = 5/12$ or 0.417 (to 3 s.f.)

ii) $5/60 \times 17/59 = 85/3540 = 17/708$ or 0.0240 (3 s.f.)

b) $13/60 \times 5/59 \times 4/58 = 260/205320 = 13/10266$ or 0.00127 (3 s.f.)

4) $6/25 \times 5/24 \times 4/23 = 120/13800 = 1/115$ or 0.00870 (3 s.f.)

5) a)

b) $0.4 \times 0.3 = 0.12$

6) a)

b) $0.3 \times 0.2 = 0.06$

c) $(0.7 \times 0.5) + (0.3 \times 0.8) = 0.59$

7) a)

b) 1/19 or 0.0526 (3 s.f.)

c) $1 - 11/19 = 8/19 = 0.421$ (3 s.f.)

8) a)

b) 0.14

c) So you need to find out:
P(rain on day 1 | no rain on day 2) = P(no rain on day 2 and rain on day 1) ÷ P(no rain on day 2)

P(no rain on day 2) = $(0.6 \times 0.14) + (0.4 \times 0.46) = 0.268$

P(no rain on day 2 and rain on day 1) = $0.14 \times 0.6 = 0.084$

So, P(rain on day 1 | no rain on day 2) = $0.084 \div 0.268 = 0.313$

9)

So you need to find out:
P(just been used | burnt) = P(burnt and just been used) ÷ P(burnt)

P(burnt) = $(0.6 \times 0.48) + (0.4 \times 0.12) = 0.336$

P(burnt and just been used) = $0.6 \times 0.48 = 0.288$
So, P(just been used | burnt) = $0.288 \div 0.336 = 0.857$ (3 d.p.)

Discrete Probability Distributions P.82

1) A discrete uniform distribution because each number has an even chance of being drawn.

2) $p^2 + 2pq + q^2$

3) Looking at the expansion for four trials, the expression for the probability that the coin lands on heads 3 times out of 4 is:
$4p^3q$

4) Let the probability of finding a damaged grape be p and the probability of finding a good grape be q.

a) For $n = 3$, the term corresponding to one damaged grape is:
$3 \times 0.15 \times 0.85^2 = 0.325$ (3 d.p.)

b) For $n = 5$, the term corresponding to two damaged grapes is:
$10 \times 0.15^2 \times 0.85^3 = 0.138$ (3 d.p.)

5) Let the probability of finding a daffodil be p, and the probability of finding a tulip be q.

a) For n = 3:
$(p +q)^3 = p^3 + 3p^2q + 3pq^2 + q^3$
Probability of 2 tulips = $3pq^2$
$= 3 \times 0.25^2 \times 0.75$
$= 0.141$ (3 d.p.)

b) We want 3 daffodils and 1 tulip. For $n = 4$, term containing p^3q is $4p^3q = 4 \times 0.75^3 \times 0.25 = 0.422$ (3 d.p.)

c) We want the terms that correspond to 3, 4 and 5 tulips. For $n = 5$, this corresponds to
$10p^2q^3 + 5pq^4 + q^5$
$= (10 \times 0.75^2 \times 0.25^3) +$
$(5 \times 0.75 \times 0.25^4) + 0.25^5$
$= 0.104$ (3 d.p.)

Mixed Questions P.83-84

1) a)

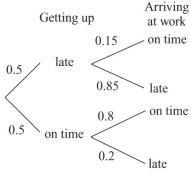

b) i) $0.5 \times 0.8 = 0.4$
ii) $(0.5 \times 0.85) + (0.5 \times 0.2)$
$= 0.525$
iii) P(got up late | late for work)
= P(got up late and late for work) ÷ P(late for work)

P(late for work) = 0.525

P(got up late and late for work)
$= 0.5 \times 0.85 = 0.425$
So, $0.425 \div 0.525$
$= 0.810$ (3 d.p.)

2) a)

	Left hand	Right hand
Caught	**26**	76
Dropped	64	**14**
Total	**90**	90

b) i) $26/90 = 13/45 = 0.289$ (3 s.f.)
ii) $14/90 = 7/45 = 0.156$ (3 s.f.)
c) i) Catches $= 102/180 = 17/30$ or 0.567 (3 s.f.)
ii) Drops $= 78/180 = 13/30$ or 0.433 (3 s.f.)
d) Catches $= 0.567 \times 70$
$= 39.7$ (3 s.f.) so 40 catches

3) a) $24/30 = 4/5 = 0.8$
b) There are two trials so use the expansion of $(p + q)^2$. Use the term $2pq$ from $p^2 + 2pq + q^2$
So, $2 \times 0.74 \times 0.26 = 0.3848$

4) a) $0.018 \times 348 = 6.264$, so around six trains will be late.
b) Subtract from one the probability of no trains being late.
So, $1 - (0.982 \times 0.982 \times 0.982 \times 0.982) = 0.0701$ (3 s.f.)
c) P(two trains being late) $= 10p^2q^3$
$= 10 \times (0.018)^2 \times (0.982)^3 = 0.00307$ (3 s.f.)

5) a) 150
b) i) $113/150 = 0.753$ (3 s.f.)
ii) $38/87 = 0.437$ (3 s.f.)
iii) $30/51 = 0.588$ (3 s.f.)

6) a) P(red) = 26/52.
P(more than 10) = 12/52.
P(red and more than 10) = 6/52.
So, P(red or more than 10) =
$26/52 + 12/52 - 3/26 = 32/52 = 0.615$ (3 s.f.)
b) $(26/52) \times (25/51) = 25/102 = 0.245$ (3 s.f.)
c) The first card can be any card, so the probability of picking any card is 1. Once you've chosen that card, the probability of picking another card with the same value is 3/51.
So, $1 \times (3/51) = 0.0588$ (3 s.f.)

CGP

ISBN 978 1 84146 599 9

9 781841 465999

MSHA42